FOR BRIAN CROUCHER AND ALL OUR ADVENTURES. ONWARDS MY FRIEND

ATLANTIS

THE LEGEND OF A LOST CITY

Adapted and retold from Plato's *Timaeus* and *Critias*

by CHRISTINA BALIT

With a note by Geoffrey Ashe

FRANCES LINCOLN

First there was Chaos.

From Chaos sprang Earth and Heaven.

From them came the race of Titans; two of them, Cronos and Rhea, seized power and ruled over all. Their son Zeus overthrew them. Then he and his brothers divided up the world: to Zeus went the heavens, to Dis the realms of the dead, while the seas and oceans went to mighty Poseidon, who promised to guard the waters with care.

Floating on one of Poseidon's emerald seas was a small rocky island. Few visited its shores and no one bothered to give it a name. But the sun rose warmly over it each morning and set sleepily behind it every night.

IN THE CENTRE of the island there stood a mountain, and at the foot of the mountain lived a man called Evenor and his wife Leucippe. They lived happily together, working hard to tend the barren land, and brought up their daughter Cleito to honour all creatures.

Poseidon grew curious. How could they be content with so little? So he took on human form and crouched behind a rock unseen, to find out.

Each morning, at daybreak, he watched Cleito walk over the pebbled ground, barefoot and smiling, to fill her water-pot at the stream.

SEEING CLEITO in all her beauty, Poseidon's heart grew tender, and one day he stepped out from behind the rock to talk to her. Slowly she began to return his love, and finally she agreed to become his bride. Her parents, unaware of Poseidon's divinity, blessed the union, and a simple wedding followed.

But a god cannot stay hidden. After the wedding, all the spirits of the sea rose to the surface to sing, and Poseidon assumed his divine form once more. He vowed to rebuild the island and make it fit for a king and his queen.

POSEIDON used powers beyond human imagining to transform the isle into a paradise.

First, he arranged alternate circles of sea and land – three of land and three of water – to enclose the mountain. Within each circle of land a forest sprang up. Trees bloomed and grew heavy with fruits. Creatures multiplied, above all the mighty elephant.

Next, he made a network of canals, fed by waterfalls. Soon the island was yielding two crops each year – one watered by winter rains, the other irrigated by Poseidon's canals. The earth was carpeted with herbs and vegetables, and thick with healing roots; from its depths men dug out priceless yellow mountain-copper. All things flourished on the sacred island.

THEN, under Poseidon's guidance, the inhabitants built a palace fit for a god, with towers, gates and parapets in white, black and red stone trimmed with gleaming brass and tin. In the centre they set up a holy temple dedicated to Poseidon and Cleito, with pinnacles of silver surrounded by a wall of gold.

They built thermal baths and aqueducts, fountains and gardens – and even a huge race-course.

I T WAS A HAPPY TIME for Poseidon and Cleito, and over the years Cleito gave birth to five pairs of twin sons. Their firstborn son they named Atlas. In the summer of his twentieth year he was crowned high king, and they named the island Atlantis in his honour.

Then Poseidon divided the island into ten parts, and gave his sons one-tenth each.

TO ENSURE PEACE in his new island city, Poseidon set down laws in stone on a pillar of the temple. Chief among them was the commandment that no person should take up arms against another – with a terrible curse on anyone who disobeyed. Every five years, Atlas and the nine princes gathered by night beside the pillar to judge their people according to Poseidon's laws. The people of Atlantis became wise, gentle, and great-spirited. They were sober and kind, as the Creator had always wanted them to be. Above all, they lived in peace.

So ATLANTIS prospered. Its splendid docks were thronged with ships and merchandise, and behind them, a towering lighthouse lit the way for incoming boats bringing cargoes from other lands. The harbours hummed with trade. Bridges and an underground canal were built to connect the three circles of land around the mountain, as the people grew ever richer.

Poseidon, watching from the waves, was content, and went away to his home at the bottom of the sea.

MANY years passed, and Atlantis began to change. Remember that the princes were descended from a god: that god now lay sleeping. Slowly, very slowly, the god-like part of their souls faded and their mortal, human natures took over. They started to argue. Gradually they lost the gift of goodness and became infected with ambition and power. Greed filled the citizens' hearts. The streets of Atlantis, once safe, became dangerous, as they began to steal, cheat and lie.

ONE DAY ZEUS, god of gods, who rules according to the law of the Creator, looked down from the heavens above. He saw the city walls crumbling with neglect, the empty temple and, worst of all, people fighting one other. He roared out his anger.

The sound of his fury woke Poseidon. Rising to the surface of the waves, the sea-god looked out over his once-perfect kingdom – and wept.

Now he had no choice: he must carry out his terrible curse.

RAISING his trident, he stirred the seas into a wave that rose so high, it lashed the heavens. The wave vibrated with a roar which could be heard two thousand miles away, and the earth trembled in terror. Then, gathering its full force, the wave crashed down upon the land, while burning ashes and rain blistered down from above.

In a single day and night, Atlantis was swallowed up by the sea.

THEN there was silence. The city sank down slowly to its new resting-place on the ocean floor.

Its people continued to exist beneath the waves, but they never spoke, or quarrelled, or fought again. As year followed year they paid a terrible penance, learning to live without gold or possessions in the cold depths. In time, they became little more than creatures of the water.

But where does Atlantis lie? Beneath which sea? Is it still there, waiting to be found?

No one knows, nor perhaps ever shall. It is an old-world story that I once heard from an aged man, a long long time ago ...

WHERE WAS ATLANTIS?

People have suggested many different places where Atlantis might once have been. The oldest Greek legends describe Atlantis as being out to the west, in the middle of the ocean – the ocean that is still named the Atlantic, after Cleito's son. The people of Atlantis are said to have spread to other countries, founding settlements in Europe and Africa, and even in a land we now call America.

Some think Atlantis existed more or less as Plato described it, and that its people left traces behind them. Egypt has pyramids, Mexico has pyramids, so perhaps the Atlantean settlers built them in both places and their submerged homeland was midway between the two countries.

Others suggest that Atlantis was closer to America. The native inhabitants of the West Indies told early explorers that their islands were once part of a single land-mass, but that a disaster long ago shattered it. The 5th-century Greek philosopher Proclus, who wanted to convince his readers that Atlantis was real, writes, very mysteriously, as if he knew of the West Indies and this tradition.

Some people suggest that Atlantis was a part of Britain. Legend tells of a sunken land between Cornwall and the Isles of Scilly.

The theory taken most seriously is that the story is actually about the island of Crete, which was highly civilised and ruled over several smaller islands. One of them, Thera, was partially destroyed in about 1450 B.C. by a tremendous eruption which also destroyed part of Crete, and its civilisation never recovered.

With so much uncertainty, some argue that the story of Atlantis is not history at all, but a myth warning us against conflict and power-seeking. Yet the legend is so vivid that many will always believe Atlantis existed ... somewhere.

Geoffrey Ashe